Specials!

Christianity

Christine Moorcroft

Acknowledgements

© 2006 Folens Limited, on behalf of the author.

United Kingdom: Folens Publishers, Apex Business Centre, Boscombe Road, Dunstable, LU5 4RL.
Email: folens@folens.com

Ireland: Folens Publishers, Greenhills Road, Tallaght, Dublin 24.
Email: info@folens.ie

Poland: JUKA, ul. Renesansowa 38, Warsaw 01-905

Editor: Joanne Mitchell   Layout artist: Book Matrix   Illustrations: Peter Wilks of SGA
Cover design: Holbrook Design   Cover image: Corbis

First published 2006 by Folens Limited.

British Library Cataloguing in Publication Data. A catalogue record for this publication is available from the British Library.

ISBN 1-84303-883-8

Contents

Introduction

Specials! RE Christianity provides ten units of work to help students with lower reading abilities to have access to the RE curriculum. Each unit is linked to the QCA scheme of work and to the 5–14 guidelines for RE.

The activities are intended for students whose reading comprehension age is between six and nine. Some activity sheets are more challenging than others; teachers will need to select accordingly.

Each unit contains four to six photocopiable activity sheets. Some of these are pages which provide background information or sources, such as newspaper articles, drawings of artefacts or passages from the Bible, hymns or prayers, should be used together with another activity sheet. They can be used in different ways, for example, students could work from them individually, in pairs or in small groups. Where necessary, vocabulary is provided on the activity sheets.

The **Teacher's notes** provide background information which gives guidance to the teacher when using the **Activity sheets**. Also included in the Teacher's notes are:

- **Objectives** (the main skills and knowledge to be learned)
- **Prior knowledge** expected of students to be familiar with already in order to complete the activity sheets
- **QCA links**
- **Scottish attainment targets**
- **Starter activities** introducing each unit or relating it to a previous topic
- Suggestions about using the **Activity sheets**
- **Plenary session** which can be undertaken to recall key points.

At the end of the book is an **Assessment sheet** to help teachers to monitor students' progress and to provide a useful self-assessment record for the students. They could complete this individually, with the teacher also completing a copy; they can then compare and discuss the two. Alternatively, the students could work in pairs on peer assessments and then compare the outcomes with one another. The assessment sheet can be used to encourage the students to discuss their own progress, consider different points of view and, with guidance, to set targets.

Looking for God

Objectives

● Show knowledge of some ways in which people seek to prove that God exists
● Identify some important or ultimate questions and suggest ways in which some people might try to answer them
● Identify the beliefs of others and state their own views in simple terms, giving reasons

Prior knowledge

The students should show awareness of some reasons why people believe in God and understand that people's beliefs are personal to them. They should also find out how people experience God in the world around them. Students should be given opportunities to develop skills of empathy, interpretation and reflection and to debate.

QCA link

Unit 7A Where do we look for God?

Scottish attainment targets

Personal search
Strand – Ultimate questions
Level C/D

Background

Julian of Norwich (1342–1413) lived in a cell close to Norwich Cathedral. She experienced a series of 'showings' during a serious illness at the age of 30 in which she believed that God communicated with her, giving her insight into the relationship between humans, nature and God.

Starter activity

Ask the students what they used to do with their teeth that fell out when they were younger. Ask them if they believed in the tooth fairy. Do they still believe in it? Discuss why they once believed this and what stopped them. Invite them to describe other beliefs which some people have but not others. Tell them that they are going to explore beliefs, including beliefs about God.

Activity sheets

'Truth'. Ask the students to cut out the cards and sort them into two sets: true or false. They could make a third set for not sure. Do they agree? Encourage them to justify their decisions. Introduce the idea of proof. Can we believe without proof?

'Believe it or not'. Following on from the previous activity, ask the students to sort the cards according to whether they believe them and, if they do, whether this is without proof. They could glue them onto the chart for others to read and comment on.

'In the news'. The students could read the newspaper reports as a group. Ask them what they think made each event happen. Could God be involved? Discuss why some people say there cannot be a God if tragedies happen.

'Acts of God' asks the students to give reasons as to why some people may believe in God and why others may not. They should use the word bank to help them.

'Meeting God' asks the students where they would look if they wanted to find God, and when. Do people really meet God? Once they have read the activity sheet, ask them what Julian of Norwich learned from this meeting with God (she called it a 'showing'). They could find out more about these showings and how they affected her belief in God.

Plenary

Explain the difference a religious belief makes to a person's life. The students could comment on the ways in which beliefs affect Christians they have met or Christians in public life.

Truth

☞ Cut out the cards. Sort them into two sets: true and false. With a partner, discuss any statements you are unsure about.

It will rain tomorrow.	$6 \times 6 = 36$
There is no such thing as a ghost.	There is a God.
One day I shall go to the moon for a holiday.	There are people on other planets.
Our school will still be here tomorrow.	There is a country named France.
We all have a soul.	Whales live in the sea.
There is a monster in Loch Ness in Scotland.	UFOs sometimes come to Earth.

Believe it or not

☞ You need the cards from 'Truth'. Sort the cards onto this chart.

I believe these because I have proof	I believe these without proof	I do not believe these

☞ What makes you believe something without proof? Talk to a partner about this. Make notes on a separate piece of paper.

Activity sheet – Looking for God

In the news

☞ Read each newspaper report. What made each event happen? Was it God?

Landslide buries village

Hundreds died this morning after a landslide buried a village in Bolivia under a sea of mud. Four bodies and seven injured villagers were dug out but hundreds of others are missing.

Child found alive after crash

A five-year-old boy has been found alive in the wreckage of the plane which crashed into mountains in Greece. He has been taken to a hospital in Athens and doctors say he is doing well.

New life after lottery

Ann Smith's lottery win will change her life. The 65-year-old will use some of her £2.2 million prize to pay for a hip replacement operation. Soon she will throw away her walking sticks.

Thousands starve in famine

The last drop of rain in Sudan fell more than six months ago. The soil is bare. A few skinny cattle roam the fields. Families bury their dead.

Dan amazes doctors

After six years of treatment for a rare bone marrow disorder, 14-year-old Dan Wilson's blood cells are starting to heal themselves. The good news comes just after a bone marrow donor was found. It's a dream come true for the Trenton boy's family.

Hope for cancer sufferers

A Manchester scientist has invented a mobile body scanner which could save the lives of cancer sufferers. Neil Marks' invention could get rid of long waits for scans. Cheap to build and light in weight, it will fit into a medium-sized van.

Acts of God

☞ What could Amy and Jack say? Write in the speech bubbles. Use the word bank to help.

I believe in God because_____

_____

_____

_____

_____

I do not believe in God because_____

_____

_____

_____

_____

Word bank			
beauty	disease	good	nature
birth	earthquakes	hurricanes	poverty
death	evil	love	war

Meeting God

Some people have felt that God was close to them.

In the 14th century, Julian of Norwich lived alone in a cell so that she could pray and meditate. She never left it. People brought food and anything else she needed.

She was very ill for a time. While she was ill, she felt that God came to her cell 16 times. She wrote that she could feel that someone was there. She could see a shape. She heard a voice talking to her. She was certain it was God.

Each time God came, he taught her something about him.

One night, God asked her to hold something little, no bigger than a hazelnut. She asked him what it was.

'It is all that exists,' he said.

She wondered how something so tiny could survive. It was so small and delicate.

She knew then that the whole universe survives because God made it. God loves it and God keeps it.

☞ Was it really God? _____

If not, who or what was it? _____

Why do you think this? _____

Teacher's notes

Christian justice

Objectives

- Recount stories about Christian leaders
- Identify and consider basic questions and ideas about who is a leader and what it means to be a follower

Prior knowledge

The students should find out about biblical stories, including some with significant leaders, and how choices in life may relate to beliefs about God and humanity. They should also show awareness of the ways in which religious people try to serve others. Students should be given opportunities to develop skills of empathy, reflection and application in RE.

QCA link

Unit 7B What does justice mean to Christians?

Scottish attainment targets

Christianity
Strand – Moral values and attitudes
Level C/E

Background

The story of Zacchaeus, who lived in Jericho, can be found in Luke 19:1–10. The story illustrates the Christian belief that, although it might seem unfair, there is more rejoicing in heaven over a sinner who repents than over people who are already doing what is right. It draws out the idea of rewarding wrongdoers who mend their ways.

Mother Teresa of Calcutta (now Kolkata) was born Agnes Gonxha Bojaxhiu on August 26, 1910, in Skopje, Macedonia, in the former Yugoslavia. When she took her vows as a Sister of Loretto, she chose the name Teresa after Saint Teresa of Lisieux. She started a school in the slums of Calcutta for poor children and learned basic medicine in order to treat poor people. She founded the Missionaries of Charity in Calcutta in 1950. She died in 1997.

Starter activity

Ask the students to read a newspaper report about a crime for which someone has been punished, for example, robbery or vandalism. Ask them if justice was done. They should explain their answers. Ask them if the same punishment should be given to anyone who commits the same crime. Is punishment necessary for justice to be done?

Activity sheets

'That's justice'. Allow about ten minutes for the students to decide whether justice is being done in each case. Invite feedback. Ask them what justice means. Is this justice for the person who did wrong, for the victims, or for both?

'Zacchaeus'. Together, read the passage. Invite feedback from the students. What injustice was there? Explain that the people of Jericho were suffering because of the high taxes they were paying, while Zacchaeus was becoming rich. How would they deal with this injustice? Tell them the rest of the story or let them read it in the Bible (Luke 19:1–10). Jesus asked Zacchaeus to take him to his house. People complained that he was favouring a sinner. Zacchaeus promised Jesus that he would sell half his belongings and give them to the poor and that if he had cheated anyone, he would pay back four times as much.

'Paul's justice' and 'Your justice'. Copy 'Paul's justice' onto an OHT and read with the students. Do the victims of wrongdoings usually respond as Paul says they should? Was Paul right? Discuss how Paul uses language to convince people. Might the people have changed their behaviour after listening to him? The students should consider the examples on 'Your justice' and apply Paul's teaching to them.

'Mother Teresa's justice'. Tell the students about the life of Mother Teresa of Calcutta. Read the passages together. Ask them how Mother Teresa's work was different from that of hospitals, social services or some charities they know. How were her views similar to those of Paul in the Bible? How did she influence others? Draw out that she did this by example: she lived a simple life and gave everything she had and all her time to people who needed help. Ask them what difference Mother Teresa might have made to the life of George Jones.

Plenary

Ask the students how Jesus was different from other people and what made him a good leader. In what ways was Mother Teresa like him?

That's justice

☞ Work in a group of five. Each person should vote on whether they feel that justice is being done in each of the four cases.

Is justice being done?

Put a tick or a cross in the boxes.

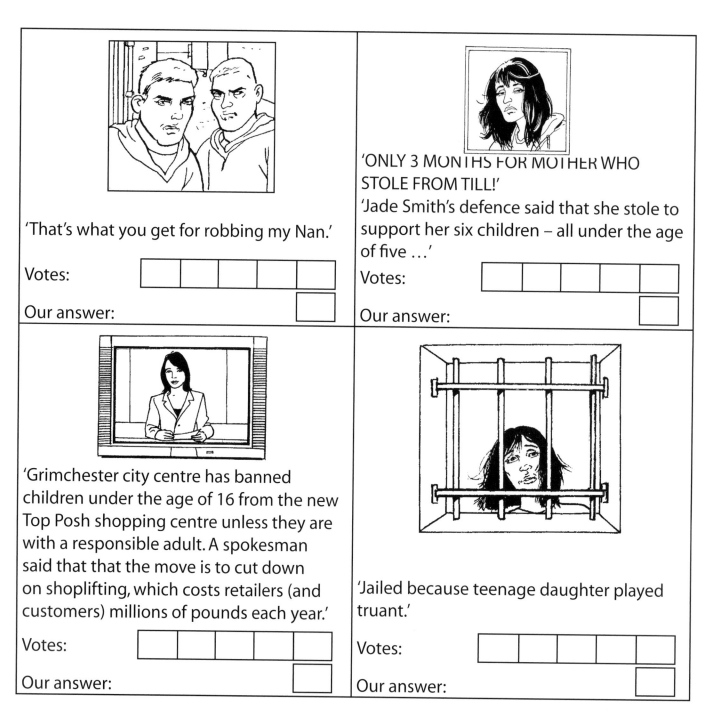

'That's what you get for robbing my Nan.'

Votes:

Our answer:

'ONLY 3 MONTHS FOR MOTHER WHO STOLE FROM TILL!'

'Jade Smith's defence said that she stole to support her six children – all under the age of five …'

Votes:

Our answer:

'Grimchester city centre has banned children under the age of 16 from the new Top Posh shopping centre unless they are with a responsible adult. A spokesman said that that the move is to cut down on shoplifting, which costs retailers (and customers) millions of pounds each year.'

Votes:

Our answer:

'Jailed because teenage daughter played truant.'

Votes:

Our answer:

☞ Choose one case to talk about with the class. Make notes on a separate piece of paper about how it shows justice or how it does not show justice.

Activity sheet – Christian justice

Zacchaeus

Crowds line the road into Jericho. News has spread that Jesus is coming. Here is what one local man has to say: 'I came early to

Jesus arrives in Jericho

get a place at the front. I hope he speaks to me.'

That is the hope of everyone here – just a word or two with Jesus.

A man arrives late – a small man dressed in fine clothes. He cannot see over the heads of the crowd. He tries to get to the front. People push him back. Why do they not let him in? They can easily see over his head.

'Zacchaeus, the tax-collector, takes too much tax from us. We are left poor,' says one woman. 'Why should we help him?'

The little man is not giving up. He's climbing a tree!

'He's coming! It's him!'

A small cloud of dust can be seen in the distance, then a man riding a donkey. A hush falls on the crowd, then, 'Yes – it is him!'

Jesus has now reached the edge of the crowd. People are calling his name, reaching out to him, asking for his blessing.

He has stopped. He is looking up into the tree.

 What should Jesus do next?

Discuss this with your group.

Write your ideas on a separate piece of paper.

Paul's justice

 Read the passages below. Discuss what you think with a partner.

> If someone has done you wrong, do not repay him with a wrong. Try to do what everyone considers to be good. Never take revenge. Instead, let God's anger do it, for the scripture says "I will take revenge, I will pay back, says the Lord."
> Romans 12:17–19

> If your enemies are hungry, feed them; if they are thirsty, give them a drink; for by doing this you will make them burn with shame. Do not let evil defeat you; instead, conquer evil with good.
> Romans 12:20

> I may be able to speak the languages of all human beings and even of angels, but if I have no love, my speech is no more than a noisy gong or a clanging bell. I may know everything and have enough faith to move a mountain, but without love I am nothing. I may give away all I have and even give up my body to be burnt – but if I have no love, this does me no good.
> 1 Corinthians 13:1–3

> Love is patient and kind; it is not jealous or boastful or proud. Love is not ill-mannered or selfish or bad-tempered. Love does not keep a record of wrongs. Love is not happy with evil but is happy with the truth.
> 1 Corinthians 13:4–6

 Is Paul right?

How does Paul use language to convince people?

Your justice

☞ Act the scenes with a partner.

What would you do if it happened to you?

If Paul were alive today, what would he say you should do?

Get off me! Clumsy idiot!	*My money has gone* / *I saw Kelly hanging around here at break. She spent a lot of money at lunchtime.*
What would I do?	What would I do?
What would Paul say?	What would Paul say?

☞ With your partner, finish this story on a separate piece of paper.

It was just beginning to go dark. Tal heard a voice. Then he saw a boy limping. He had blood on his face. It was Greg. Greg and his gang had called Tal names last week. They had thrown things at him…

Specials! RE Christianity

Mother Teresa's justice

This is how Mother Teresa of Calcutta (now Kolkata) described her work:

> We are not social workers. We want to bring the joy and love of God to the people; we want to bring them God himself, who gives them his love through us. At the same time we love God and show him our love by serving him in this people. There are a lot of institutions caring for the sick. We do not want to be one of them. We have to be more, to give more. We have to give ourselves. We have to bring God's love to the people by our service. And the poor people know, through us, what it really means to love and to serve God, although our full understanding will only come after we die.

This is what she said when she was given the Nobel Prize for Peace in 1979:

> I choose the poverty of our poor people. But I am grateful to receive the Nobel Prize in the name of the hungry, the naked, the homeless, the crippled, the blind, the lepers, all who feel unwanted, unloved, uncared-for – people who have become a burden to society and are shunned by everyone.

 How did Mother Teresa influence others?

In what ways are her views similar to those of Paul in the Bible?

Village protest

For two months, George Jones and his dog, Jack, have been sleeping in a tent on the village green at Little Snobbery. Local householders have objected: 'I'm trying to sell my house. People take one look at him and they are off!' said Ima Meeny, 36. 'It's an eyesore. There are hostels for people like him,' said Major Luke Down. Jones, 49, of no fixed address, does not want to live in a hostel, 'I can't take Jack with me and I don't want to leave him. He's my only friend.'

Welcome to Little Snobbery

 How might Mother Teresa have helped George Jones?

Jesus

Objectives

- Know about the time when a religious leader lived and describe some of the key events in his or her life
- Know about the person's beliefs and teachings
- Make links between religious symbols, stories and beliefs
- Make informed responses to other people's values and commitments, reflect on questions about the meaning and purpose of human existence; formulate responses to such questions

Prior knowledge

The students should learn the technical terminology within the study of Christianity, for example, disciple, heaven, Holy Spirit, prophet, saviour and so on. They should also find out about the different key beliefs and practices, and use sources to find out about a key figure. Students should be given opportunities to develop skills of interpretation and reflection.

QCA link

Unit 7C Religious figure

Scottish attainment targets

Christianity
Strand – Sacred writings, stories and key figures
Level D;
Strand – Beliefs
Level D

Background

Jesus was a real person who lived about 2000 years ago in the area now known as Israel and Palestine. No one knows what he looked like. References have been found about him in several ancient sources, including the descriptions 'Christ' and 'Son of Man'. He is mentioned in the Qur'an as well as the Bible. Muslims regard him as a prophet.

Starter activity

Show the students images of Jesus: icons, paintings, sculptures, statuettes and illustrations from children's Bibles. Point out that no one knows what he looked like because there are no portraits of him from his lifetime. What personal qualities do the images suggest? (Examples: authority, calm, gentleness, humility, intelligence.)

Activity sheets

'What do we know about Jesus?' asks the students to jot down anything they know about Jesus. This need not be in the form of sentences; it could be in single words. Encourage them to think about Bible stories, hymns and prayers they know and about posters they might have seen outside churches. In groups, they should explain why they wrote each word. On a large sheet of paper, each group should write the four words they think best describe Jesus. Invite a spokesperson from each group to tell the others why they chose these words. Encourage them to justify their answers with evidence.

'A special birth' provides information about the birth of Jesus. How did people at the time know he was going to be special? After reading the passages, they should highlight the words which suggest that Jesus was to be special in some way.

'Sources' and 'Finding out from sources'. After looking at the sources, students should look for evidence to reach four conclusions as to what Jesus was like. How did Jesus support poor people? How did he help those who were insulted? Draw out that he supported people in need and anyone who was a victim of other people's hate, meanness or unfairness and so on. Discuss the meaning of hypocrisy and how Jesus dealt with it. Were the students surprised that Jesus acted angrily? Discuss what made him angry.

'Jesus the teacher' and 'What Jesus taught'. Before the students begin work on these, ask them what they think 'heaven' and 'the kingdom of God' mean. Ask the students to read each of the passages on 'Jesus the teacher' and to discuss what each means. They can provide a summary of each passage. Ask them to choose a passage which they think might help the people seen on 'What Jesus taught'.

Plenary

Ask the students what they have learned about the character of Jesus.

What do we know about Jesus?

☞ In the boxes, write three things you know about Jesus.

☞ In groups, discuss your answers.

What do you think made Jesus special?

Specials! RE Christianity

© Folens (copiable page)

Activity sheet – Jesus

A special birth

☞ Read the passages.

> God sent an angel named Gabriel to a young woman named Mary. He said, 'Peace be with you. The Lord is with you and has blessed you.'
> Mary was troubled by this and wondered what it meant. The angel told her not to be afraid. 'You are going to have a son. You will name him Jesus. He will be great. He will be the son of God. He will be a king and his kingdom will never end.
> 'But how can this be? I am a virgin,' said Mary.
> 'The holy spirit will rest upon you. For this reason the child will be called the son of God,' said the angel.
> Luke 1:27–35

> On the night when Jesus was born, some shepherds were looking after their sheep in a field. An angel came and said, 'Your saviour has been born today in Bethlehem. Go and worship him. You will find him lying in a manger in a stable.'
> A host of angels filled the sky and sang praises to God … and then they were gone.
> Luke 2:8–15

> Some men who studied the stars came from the east to Jerusalem. They asked, 'Where is he who has been born king of the Jews? We saw his star in the east and have come to worship him.'
> Herod was king of Judea at that time. When he heard about this he called the chief priests and rabbis. He asked them where this saviour had been born. 'In Bethlehem,' they said. 'For the prophet wrote, "From Bethlehem will come a leader who will guide my people Israel."'
> Matthew 2:1–6

☞ How can you tell that Jesus was going to be special?
Write three reasons on a separate piece of paper.

Activity sheet – Jesus

Sources

We know about some of the things Jesus did from what some of his followers wrote. Their writings are the gospels Matthew, Mark, Luke and John.

Jesus went to the temple with his disciples.

Beware the doctors of the law who say long prayers and walk around in long robes to look good.

This poor widow has given more than them. They have plenty, but this coin is all she had.

Children came to listen to Jesus. His disciples tried to turn them away.

If you are as open and trusting as these children, you will have a great chance of entering heaven.

One day, Jesus saw money lenders and merchants in the temple.

The Scripture says 'My house shall be a house of prayer'. You are making it a den of robbers.

Specials! RE Christianity

Finding out from sources

☞ Use the information on 'Sources' to find out what Jesus was like.

You could also use evidence from the Bible.

What Jesus was like	Evidence

Specials! RE Christianity

Jesus the teacher

☞ What did Jesus teach people about God?

Find out from these passages from the Bible. Write your answers on a separate piece of paper.

Do not worry about the food you need to stay alive or about the clothes you need for your body. Life is much more important than food, and the body is much more important than clothes. Your Father knows you need these things. He will provide you with these things.
Matthew 6:25–34

Not everyone who calls me 'Lord' will enter the kingdom of heaven, but only those who do what my Father in heaven wants them to do.
Matthew 7:21

It will be very hard for rich people to enter the kingdom of heaven. It is much harder for a rich person to enter the kingdom of God than for a camel to go through the eye of a needle.
Matthew 19:23–24

Happy are you poor; the kingdom of God is yours!
Happy are you who are hungry now; you will be filled!
Happy are you who weep now; you will laugh!
Happy are you when people hate you, reject you, insult you and say that you are evil.
Be glad when that happens and dance for joy, because a great reward is kept for you in heaven.
Luke 6:20–23

What Jesus taught

☞ With a partner, discuss what could make these people feel better.

In the speech bubbles, write what Jesus might say to each person.

Below the pictures, write what he might do.

The passages on 'Jesus the teacher' will help.

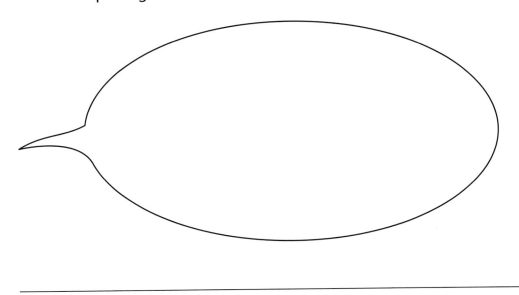

_____

_____

_____

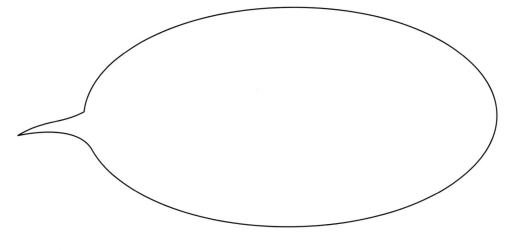
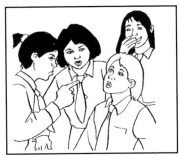

_____

_____

_____

Teacher's notes

Jesus' Incarnation and Christians today

Objectives

- Describe the main Christian beliefs associated with Christmas, understand some basic questions about human experience posed by the Christmas story and celebrations, and consider their own response to such questions
- Identify the beliefs of others and express views, giving at least one reason

Prior knowledge

The students should know about the Christmas story and celebrations. They should also show awareness of why Christmas is important to Christians, and the ways in which some religious people try to serve others in their local community.

QCA link

Unit 8A What does Jesus' Incarnation mean for Christians today?

Scottish attainment targets

Christianity
Strand – Celebrations, festivals, ceremonies and customs
Level E

Background

The Christian belief is that Jesus was born to save the world from sin. The Gospels refer to his ancestry (a descendant of King David, who is mentioned in the Old Testament and presented as the ideal king of Israel). David was the son of Jesse, who was the grandson of Ruth and Boaz (Ruth 4:17–22). The prophet Isaiah foretold the coming of Jesus 'the Messiah' who would be the saviour of the people.

Starter activity

On the flip chart, write the word 'rescue' and invite a volunteer to read it aloud. Ask the students what comes to mind when they hear this word. Explain that 'rescue' usually means being saved from something harmful.

Activity sheets

'Rescue'. After reading the story, ask the students why Grace Darling became famous. Draw out that she risked her life in order to save others. The students could collect newspaper and magazine articles about people saving others. Discuss what they were saved from and introduce the idea that people can be saved from themselves. What does this mean?

'Sin'. Discuss what 'sin' means. Are all wrongdoings sins? 'Sin' is usually a religious term meaning a wrong against God. After having read the passages from the Bible, ask the students to identify the wrongs people were doing. Encourage them to explain their answers. They should then complete the table to reach a conclusion about each of the six passages. Isaiah warned people of God's judgement and the ways in which they would suffer for their sins. Discuss what might stop people committing sins. Is there any hope for them?

'Prophecies'. On the flip chart, write the word 'prophet' and 'profit' and ask the students if they know what each word means. Can they deduce what a prophecy is and what 'to prophesy' means? Tell them that Isaiah prophesied the birth of Jesus, the Messiah. Help them to look up the meaning of 'messiah' and explain that kings were anointed. What does this say about Jesus? After reading the passages, ask them to consider how the Messiah was to change the world. They could compare the vocabulary in these passages with that of the passages in 'Sin'. Help them to identify the significant words and phrases. Discuss and explain the symbols and comparisons used, for example, light, shadow, like a tree. They could highlight these before completing the table.

'The name of Jesus' informs the students of the names used for Jesus which will help them to understand the Christian beliefs about him. 'Saviour' literally means one who saves; Christians believe that Jesus was born to save people from their sins. 'Light of the world' is a metaphor used in the gospels of John and Mark for Jesus because he was sent by God to lead people to light (representing good) and out of darkness (representing evil). 'Lamb of God' is a metaphor which means that Jesus was like a sacrificial lamb slain as an offering to God for sins to be forgiven. 'Messiah' means the anointed one. Jesus is sometimes referred to as King of the Jews; kings were considered to be God's representatives and were anointed with holy oil. Christians believe that Jesus was the son of God – a title given to kings and faithful Jews in the Old Testament; when applied to Jesus, it means the existence of a divine being in human form.

Plenary

Ask the students what they have learned about Christian beliefs about Jesus.

Rescue

The SS Forfarshire left Hull in fine weather on 5 September 1838. As the ship sailed up the east coast of England, the sea became rougher and, just south of the Farne Islands, its engine stopped. The ship began to drift. The waves became higher and stronger. Water crashed over the decks.

The captain struggled to steer the ship towards a sheltered channel of water between the islands and the open sea. He was no match for the waves. There was a great crash as the ship hit a rock. It began to break up. There was no time to reach the passengers who were still in their cabins.

Meanwhile, in the nearby Longstone lighthouse, William Darling and his family slept. But Grace, his 23-year-old daughter, had been woken by the noise of the storm. She looked out of the window. What was that dark mass out on Great Harcar rock? It must be a ship. She ran to wake her father. They strained their eyes to see through the mist and darkness.

'It's a ship! There are people on the rocks!' said William.

They were sure that it would be too rough for the lifeboats on the mainland to put to sea. They must do their best with their rowing boat. It was a strong, heavy boat and really needed three people to row it. William and Grace rowed with all their might. They finally reached the rock. The only way William could get onto the rocks was to wait for a wave to pass and then to jump. Grace had to take both oars and row backwards and forwards. This kept the boat in the same place.

On the rock, William found eight men, one was badly injured. There was a woman holding two children, but both were dead. There was also a dead man. William and three of the men rowed the boat back to the lighthouse. They took Grace, the injured man and the woman. Then they went back for the other four men.

By 11:00am, the North Sunderland lifeboat had seen the ship and put to sea. They found no survivors and stopped at the lighthouse for shelter. Imagine their surprise when they found it crowded with people! By then, Mrs Darling had lit the fire and given everyone dry clothes and hot food.

☞ Why did Grace Darling become famous?

Discuss the idea that people might need to be saved from themselves.

Sin

The prophet Isaiah lived in Jerusalem in the eighth century BCE. He told people the words of God.

You will be sorry that you ever worshipped trees.
Isaiah 1:29

A day is coming when human pride will be ended ... Idols will disappear.
Isaiah 2:12, 18

Moneylenders oppress my people and their creditors cheat them.
Isaiah 3:12

Look how proud the women of Jerusalem are! They walk with their noses in the air. They are always flirting. They take dainty little steps and the bracelets on their ankles jingle. But I will punish them – I will shave their heads and make them bald.
Isaiah 3:16–17

You are doomed. You buy more houses and fields to add to those you already have. Soon there will be nowhere for anyone else to live.
Isaiah 5:8

You get up early in the morning to start drinking and you spend long evenings getting drunk.
Isaiah 5:11

☞ On a separate piece of paper, copy and complete the table below.

What the people of Israel were doing.	Is this a sin? Explain your answer.	The changes they needed to make, if any.

Prophecies

Isaiah prophesied the coming of a Messiah – one who would save the world from sin.

> The people who walked in darkness have seen a great light.
>
> They lived in a land of shadows but now light is shining on them.
>
> Isaiah 9:2

> A child is born to us!
>
> A son is given to us!
>
> And he will be our ruler.
>
> He will be called 'Wonderful Counsellor', 'Mighty God', 'Eternal Father', 'Prince of Peace'.
>
> His royal power will grow; his kingdom will always be at peace.
>
> Isaiah 9:6–7

> The royal line of David is like a tree that has been cut down; but just as new branches
>
> sprout from a stump, so a new king will arise from among David's descendants.
>
> The spirit of the Lord will give him wisdom,
>
> and the knowledge and skill to rule his people.
>
> Isaiah 11:1–2

> Wolves and sheep will live together in peace,
>
> and leopards will lie down with young goats.
>
> Calves and lion cubs will feed together,
>
> and little children will take care of them.
>
> Isaiah 11:6

☞ What differences do these texts say the Messiah will make?

On a separate piece of paper, copy and complete the table below.

Before the Messiah comes	After the Messiah comes

The name of Jesus

☞ What names for Jesus can you find in the quotations in the table?

Underline the names.

Discuss them with your group.

Complete the table below.

Quotation	Why Jesus was given these names
This very day in David's town your Saviour was born – Christ the Lord. Luke 2:11	
I am the light of the world. Whoever follows me will have the light of life and will never walk in darkness. John 8:12	
There is the Lamb of God, who takes away the sin of the world! John 1:29	
Are you the Messiah, the Son of the Blessed God? Mark 14:61	

☞ Underline the parts of this prayer which show Christian beliefs about Jesus.

We give you thanks, O God,
for the gift to the world of our Redeemer;
as we sing your glory at the close of this day,
so may we know His presence in our hearts,
who is our Saviour and our Lord,
now and for ever.

What names for Jesus can you find in this prayer? Look up the meanings of any new ones.

The Resurrection and Christians today

Objectives

- Show some knowledge and understanding of Easter and Christian beliefs
- Identify and consider basic questions about human existence posed in the Easter stories and celebrations

Prior knowledge

The students should know of the main events in the life of Jesus. They should also show awareness and find out about interpretation of how festivals are celebrated in the light of traditional stories. Students should be given opportunities to develop skills of empathy, interpretation and reflection.

QCA link

Unit 8B What does the Resurrection of Jesus mean for Christians today?

Scottish attainment targets

Christianity
Strand – Sacred writings, stories and key figures
Level E;
Strand – Celebrations, festivals, ceremonies and customs
Level D;
Strand – Beliefs
Level E

Background

The date of Easter varies. For most Christian denominations, Easter Sunday is the first Sunday after the full moon which happens on, or the next one after, 21 March (the spring equinox). If the full moon is on a Sunday, Easter Sunday is the following Sunday.

Holy Week begins with Palm Sunday, the Sunday before Easter, a joyful celebration of the entry of Jesus into Jerusalem, which foretells the entry of the faithful into the Kingdom of Heaven. Good Friday commemorates the day when Jesus was crucified. Easter Sunday celebrates the day when it was discovered that his body was no longer in the tomb and that he had arisen from the dead.

Resurrection, in Christian belief, is explained in Paul's first letter to the Corinthians (1 Corinthians 15:36–42).

Starter activity

Show works of art depicting the Resurrection, for example, *Resurrection* (Piero della Francesca, 1463–5, Pinacoteca Comunale, Sansepolcro, Italy), *The Resurrection* (Michelangelo, 1530, Sistine Chapel, Rome), *Christ Appearing to the Apostles after the Resurrection* (William Blake, 1795), *The Morning of the Resurrection* (Edward Burne Jones, 1882), and *Resurrection at Cookham* (Stanley Spencer, 1924–6), all in the Tate Britain, London. Ask the students what the artists are saying about the Resurrection of Christ. What does 'Resurrection' mean?

Activity sheets

'The Easter story'. Allocate a different gospel (a simple version) to pairs of students and ask them to read the account of the Crucifixion, death, burial and Resurrection of Jesus. Explain that the gospels were written by four different people but not immediately after the events. Ask the students to write notes on the flow chart of the main events of the day when Jesus was crucified. Draw out the similarities between the gospels. What facts have they found? Discuss why different details are recorded in different gospels. Ask them if they celebrate Easter and if so, how. Do they celebrate it in a religious way?

'Easter cards'. Provide a collection of secular and religious Easter cards and ask the students to look for the common symbols. Discuss why these are used. Draw out that the most important Christian symbol is the cross.

'Similarities and differences'. Ask the students to read the main events of the Easter story and to record the similarities and differences in two different gospels.

'The case of the missing body' asks the students to discuss what might have happened to the body of Jesus and helps them to organise their ideas.

'Resurrection' provides the words of a joyful Christian Easter hymn and introduces vocabulary connected with the Resurrection. Ask the students to find out the meaning of these words. They should also decide what the hymn tells them about Christian beliefs.

'Life after death' asks the students to carry out a survey, asking people their thoughts about life after death. The students should discuss their results and answer the questions.

Plenary

Ask the students why, in Christian belief, Jesus had to die and then rise again to save people from their sins.

Activity sheet – The Resurrection and Christians today

The Easter story

The gospels recount what happened on the day when Jesus was crucified.

☞ Work with a partner.

Each read the account in a different gospel.

On the flow chart, make a note of the main events.

The gospels are the books of Matthew, Mark, Luke and John in the New Testament.

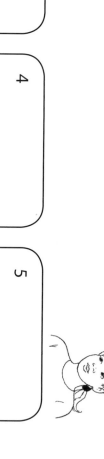

1

2

3

4

5

Specials! RE Christianity © Folens (copiable page)

Easter cards

☞ Look at four Easter cards. Number the cards 1–4. Look at the pictures and symbols. Read the words. Fill in the chart.

Card	Picture	Symbols	What they symbolise	Important words
1				
2				
3				
4				

Similarities and differences

☞ Read the main events of the story of the first Easter ('The Easter story') .

   Record the similarities and differences between two different gospels.

Gospels: _____ and _____	
Similarities	**Differences**

☞ Compare your answers with those of others who read different gospels.

   On a separate piece of paper, list the main facts and the main things people wrote.

The case of the missing body

☞ What could have happened to the body of Jesus?

Discuss this with your group.

List all the explanations you can think of and vote for the most probable one. | **X** |

Explanation	

☞ Which do you think is the most likely? _____

_____

Explain why _____

_____

_____

Resurrection

Look up any words you do not understand.

☞ Read the hymn below with a partner.

Discuss what it means.

In the boxes on the right below, explain the meanings of the bold words in the hymn.

Jesus Christ is **risen** today, Alleluya!
Our triumphant holy day, Alleluya!
Who did once upon the Cross, Alleluya!
Suffer to redeem our loss. Alleluya!

Hymns of praise then let us sing, Alleluya!
Unto Christ, our heavenly King, Alleluya!
Who endured the Cross and grave, Alleluya!
Sinners to **redeem** and save. Alleluya!

But the pains that he endured, Alleluya!
Our **salvation** have procured, Alleluya!
Now above the sky he's King, Alleluya!
Where the angels ever sing. Alleluya!

By Lyra Davidica (1708)

☞ What does the hymn tell you about Christian beliefs?

_____

_____

_____

_____

Life after death

☞ Find out what people you know think about life after death.

Ask them the questions below. (You will need more than one copy of this activity sheet.)

Tick the boxes.

Count the ticks in each box to show what most of the people in your survey believe.

	Yes	No	Don't know
Do we have something which lives on after our bodies die?			
Do you believe in heaven?			
Do you believe in hell?			
If we pray for someone who dies, can this help them after death?			
Do people meet God when they die?			
Do they meet Jesus?			
Do they meet others who have died?			
Does what you do during your lifetime matter after you die?			

☞ Discuss the answers with your group.

What do most of the people in your survey believe about life after death?

_____

_____

What do you believe? _____

_____

_____

Teacher's notes

Christian beliefs and practice

Objectives

- Show some knowledge and understanding of the main Christian beliefs and practices and what belonging to a religious community involves
- Understand the meaning of some religious symbols and use some religious technical language correctly
- Identify the beliefs of others and give at least one reason for agreeing or disagreeing with them

Prior knowledge

The students should show awareness of some religious beliefs and practices and understand that belief in God affects people's behaviour. They should also find out the ways in which religious people try to serve others. They should be given opportunities to develop skills of empathy, interpretation and reflection and to agree and disagree with others in a constructive way.

QCA link

Unit 8C Beliefs and practice

Scottish attainment targets

Christianity
Strand – Sacred places, worship and symbols
Level D;
Strand – Beliefs
Level D

Background

The cross symbolises the death and resurrection of Christ. Three steps below a cross represent, from top to bottom, the Christian virtues of faith, hope and charity. Rosary beads are used mainly by Roman Catholics as an aid to concentration during prayer. The dove symbolises the Holy Spirit (Mark 1:10). The fish represents Christ (the Greek word for fish 'ichthus' came to stand for Iesu Christos Theou Uios Soter, which means 'Jesus Christ, God's Son, Saviour'.

Starter activity

Show some symbols in everyday use, for example, road signs, health and safety warning symbols, washing instruction labels. Ask the students what they mean. Why do we use symbols instead of words? Explain that symbols can convey meaning more quickly than text. Note that symbols have to be understood by everyone using them. Ask the students about any symbols they use, with whom, and why they use them. Explain that a shared symbol can create a sense of belonging to a group and that the symbol can remind the group of an important event, action or belief. Also enquire about words and sayings which have special meanings for the students.

Activity sheets

'Artefacts'. Show the students some Christian artefacts and ask what they mean to Christians. If necessary, explain the symbolism in appropriate detail. The students should then complete the table using the word bank to help them.

'This is God'. Together, read the passages. Explain 'condemn', 'eternally' and 'salvation'. Draw attention to the sources of the quotations (books of the Bible) and ask the students to discuss, with a partner, what they can find out from them about the Christian view of God.

'Hymns'. Together, read the lines from hymns. Explain that Christians believe that Christ died and rose again so that they could be forgiven for their sins; that God is male, the creator, and provides for people's needs; he is merciful and just, unchanging and everlasting and Christians address him as a father; people who are truly sorry for their sins will enter the kingdom of heaven. This is also an opportunity for the students to explore their own beliefs about God.

'Prayers'. After reading the prayers, focus on the first prayer and ask the students what they think this prayer is for (to say they are sorry for their sins and to ask God to forgive them). They should match a purpose to each prayer. Point out that some prayers have more than one purpose. (Answers: 1C, 2B, 3ABC, 4E.)

Plenary

Discuss what we can learn from Christian worship about the main beliefs of Christianity.

Artefacts

☞ To complete the table, list the places where you have seen symbols like these.

What do the symbols make you think of?

What do they mean for Christians?

Use the word bank to help you.

Word bank				
Christ	cross	crucified	dove	Easter
fish	Greek	Holy Spirit	Jesus	peace
pure	salvation	Saviour	Son of God	

Symbol	Where seen	What it makes me think of	What it means for Christians
✝			
𓆝			
🕊			

This is God

☞ Read the passages below.

What do Christians think God is like?

On a separate piece of paper, list words to describe God.

Underline the words from the Bible passages below which make you think this.

The Lord is my light and my salvation;
I will fear no one.
The Lord protects me from all danger;
I will never be afraid.
Psalms 27:1

The Lord says,
'I will condemn those
who turn away from me
and put their trust in human beings,
in the strength of mortals.'
Jeremiah 17:5

O Lord, you have always been our home.
Before you created the hills
or brought the world into being,
you were eternally God,
and will be God for ever.
Psalms 90:1–2

Our God is merciful and tender.
He will cause the bright dawn of
salvation to rise on us
and to shine from heaven on all those
who live in the dark shadow of death,
to guide our steps into the path of
peace.
Luke 1:78–79

Everything that happens in this world
happens at a time God chooses.
Ecclesiastes 3:1

The Lord is ready to judge his people.
Isaiah 3:13

God's divine power has given us
everything we need to live a truly
religious life. He has given us the very
great and precious gifts he promised.
2 Peter 1:3–4

Activity sheet – Christian beliefs and practice

Hymns

☞ What can you find out about Christian beliefs from these hymns?

Underline the words which show each belief.

You could use a different colour for each belief.

Hymn	Belief
The Cross! It takes our guilt away; It holds the fainting spirit up. (*We sing the praise of him who died*)	
Christ the Lord is risen again! Alleluya! (*Christ the Lord is risen again*)	
Praise God, from whom all blessings flow, Praise Him, all creatures here below, (*Awake my soul, and with the sun*)	
Swift to its close ebbs out life's little day; Earth's joys grow dim, its glories pass away; Change and decay in all around I see; O Thou who changest not, abide with me. (*Abide with me*)	
Blest are the pure in heart, For they shall see our God, The secret of the Lord is theirs, Their soul is Christ's abode. (*Blest are the pure in heart*)	
Saviour breathe forgiveness o'er us, All our weakness Thou dost know; Thou didst tread this earth before us, Thou didst feel its keenest woe; (*Saviour breathe forgiveness o'er us*)	
Let us with a gladsome mind, Praise the Lord for He is kind: For His mercies aye endure, Ever faithful, ever sure. (*Let us with a gladsome mind*)	
Praise to the Lord, the Almighty, the King of creation; O my soul, praise Him, for He is thy health and salvation: (*Praise to the Lord, the Almighty, the King of creation*)	

Prayers

☞ What is the purpose of prayer for Christians?

Match the purposes to the prayers by putting the letters in the appropriate boxes.

Some prayers may have more than one purpose.

A	To praise God	E	To thank God
B	To ask for protection from danger	F	To ask God to look after others
C	To ask God for forgiveness	G	To ask for help
D	To ask for God's blessing	H	To ask for peace

1. Lord God,

 we have sinned against you;

 we have done evil in your sight.

 We are sorry and repent.

Purpose:

2. Lighten our darkness,

 Lord, we pray;

 and in your great mercy defend us

 from all perils and dangers of this night;

 for the love of your only Son,

 our Saviour Jesus Christ.

Purpose:

3. Our Father in heaven,

hallowed be your name,

your will be done,

on earth as it is in heaven.

Give us today our daily bread.

Forgive us our sins

as we forgive those who sin against us.

Save us from the time of trial

and deliver us from evil.

For the kingdom, the power,

and the glory are yours

now and for ever.

Purpose:

4. Almighty God, Father of all mercies,

 we your unworthy servants give you most

 humble and hearty thanks

 for all your goodness and loving kindness

 to us and to all men.

 We bless you for our creation,

 preservation,

 and all the blessings of this life…

Purpose:

Teacher's notes

A visit to a church

Objectives

- Describe a church using some correct terms and explain what it is used for
- Know what Christianity believes about God and express their own ideas about God in response
- Talk about places which are special to them

Prior knowledge

The students should know some technical terminology specific to Christianity and make connections between key beliefs and practice. They should also use artefacts and pictures as sources, particularly through previous visits to places of worship. Students should be given opportunities to develop skills of empathy, interpretation and reflection and to agree and disagree with others in a constructive way.

QCA link

Unit 8E A visit to a place of worship

Scottish attainment targets

Christianity
Strand – Sacred places, worship and symbols
Level C

Background

Churches vary in some ways, but they all contain an altar (which is the focal point, approached only by the priest, with pews or seats facing it either in rows or in a circle or semicircle), a cross or crucifix and a Bible. They may also have stained-glass windows which tell Bible stories or show scenes from the scriptures. In Anglican and Roman Catholic churches there is usually a font which may be near the entrance or in front of where the congregation sits. This is where children are baptised. In Baptist churches there is an immersion pool in which adults are baptised.

Starter activity

Ask the students about any places which are special to them. What makes them special? Focus on places associated with specific activities. Ask them where they would go if they wanted to think about or reflect on anything, for example, to sort out worries or relationships or to remember someone who had died. What qualities does the place have?

Activity sheets

'Church features'. Ask the students how they can tell that a building is a church. What special features does it have (inside and outside)? The students should label each feature on the activity sheet, and write what its purpose is in relation to how it helps Christians to worship God, for example, there are pews because Christians sit during church services. (Answers: The hymn boards tell them which hymns are to be sung. Hassocks (kneelers), because some Christians kneel when praying. The altar is the holiest part of the church, approached only by the priest or minister – it is reminiscent of the altars on which lambs or other animals were once offered to God as sacrifices.)

'Church sense' helps the students to prepare for a visit to a church. They could describe the ways in which they behave in another place of worship. Draw out the similarities, for example, showing respect for a holy place. Draw out any differences and the reason for them, for example, in some places of worship it is appropriate for both men and women to cover their heads or remove their shoes.

'In the church'. The students should note what they see, hear, smell and feel during their visit to a church.

'Questionnaire' helps the students to prepare for note-taking by articulating what they know and what they want to find out.

'Holy Communion'. Explain that Holy Communion is a very important act of worship which commemorates the Crucifixion. The activity sheet provides a passage from the Bible which refers to the origin of Holy Communion and what it symbolises. The students should answer the questions.

'Church plan' requires the students to create a church plan. They should draw a plan and cut out and glue on the features. This activity sheet will focus the students on the significant parts of a church.

Plenary

Invite some students to choose a feature of a church to describe and to explain why it is important. What can they learn from it about Christian beliefs?

Church features

☞ Label the pictures. Use the word bank to help you.
What are they for?

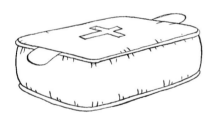

| 195 |
| 87 |
| 306 |
| 220 |

Purpose: _____

_____

_____

Purpose: _____

_____

_____

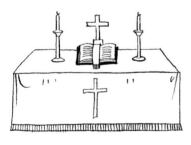

Purpose: _____

_____

_____

| **Word bank** | | |
| altar | hassock | hymn board |

Church sense

☞ How should you behave in a church? Why?

Discuss this with your group.

Complete the table.

What to wear	Why
How to move around the church	Why
Where to go and what to touch	Why

In the church

☞ What can you see, hear, smell and feel in the church?

Make notes on each notepad.

See

Hear

Smell

Feel

Specials! RE Christianity

© Folens (copiable page)

Questionnaire

☞ Plan some questions you will ask about the church.

Feature of a church	What I know about it	What I want to know	Answer

What people do in church	What I know about it	What I want to know	Answer

Holy Communion

☞ What happens at Holy Communion?

_____

_____

_____

☞ What do these items represent?

Communion wafers   Bread   Wine

_____   _____   _____

☞ This passage from the Bible tells about the Last Supper. This was when Jesus celebrated the Passover with his disciples just before he was crucified. Underline the words which explain what Christians remember at Holy Communion.

When the hour came, Jesus took his place at the table with the apostles. He said to them, 'I have wanted so much to eat this Passover meal with you before I suffer! For I tell you, I will never eat it until it is given its full meaning in the Kingdom of God.'

Then Jesus took a cup, gave thanks to God, and said, 'Take this and share it among yourselves. I tell you that from now on I will not drink this wine until the Kingdom of God comes.'

Then he took a piece of bread, gave thanks to God, broke it, and gave it to them, saying, 'This is my body, which is given for you. Do this in memory of me.'

In the same way, he gave them the cup after supper, saying, 'This cup is God's new covenant sealed with my blood, which is poured out for you.'
Luke 22:14–20

Church plan

☞ Draw a plan of a church.

Cut out these objects and glue them onto the plan.

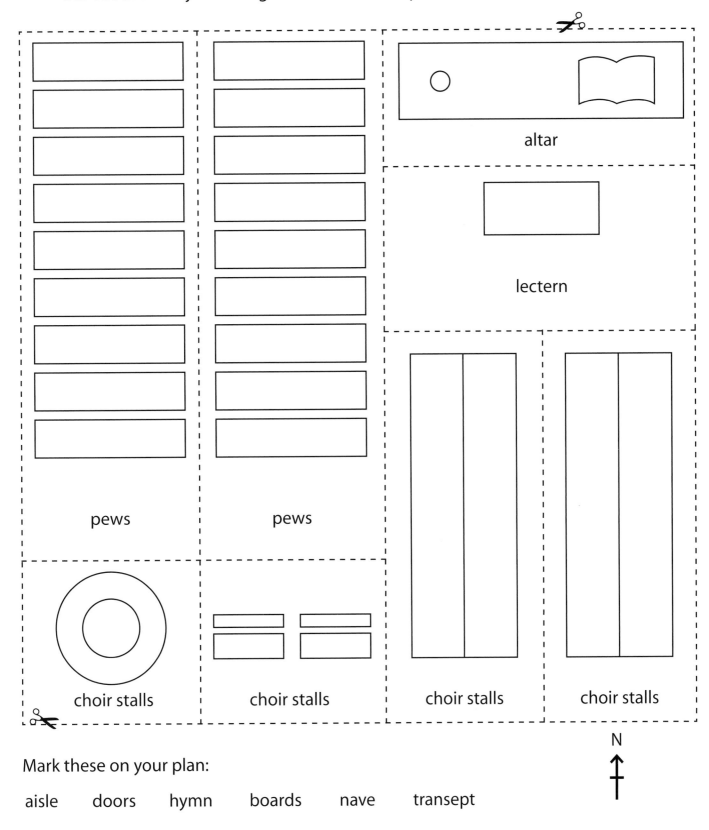

altar

lectern

pews

pews

choir stalls

choir stalls

choir stalls

choir stalls

N

Mark these on your plan:

aisle   doors   hymn   boards   nave   transept

Teacher's notes

Rites of passage

Objectives

- Show that they know and understand some Christian rites of passage and understand how belonging to a religion affects people's lives at certain times Make informed responses to religious ceremonies, explaining their importance to a believer
- Reflect on the nature of commitment and think about their own individual commitments

Prior knowledge

The students should know of technical terminology specific to Christianity. They should also interpret source materials from faith communities, taking account of different perspectives. Students should also be given opportunities to develop skills of empathy, interpretation and reflection and to agree and disagree with others in a constructive way.

QCA link

Unit 9A Where are we going? Rites of passage

Scottish attainment targets

Christianity
Strand – Celebrations, festivals, ceremonies and customs
Level D

Background

Rites of passage have long been used in different religions and cultures to integrate biological events (birth, reproduction and death) with spiritual experience. They celebrate the connection between an individual and the community, giving meaning to that experience. In some Christian denominations, babies are baptised; in others baptism takes place when an individual can understand its significance. A dedication ceremony is held for infants, to dedicate them to Jesus. Some Christians are confirmed at about 13 years of age: they renew, and take responsibility for keeping, the baptism promises. All Christian groups, like other religious groups, hold a funeral service for those who die.

Starter activity

The students could bring in items associated with 'milestones' in their lives. Ask them about these events. They could arrange them on a time line. Were they celebrated? How?

Activity sheets

'Baptism symbols'. Ask the students how babies are welcomed into families. Students from religious backgrounds could describe any ceremonies they took part in. Note that welcoming a new baby into a religious community can involve the use of symbols. The students should write the meanings of each of the baptism symbols on the activity sheet.

'Baptism ceremony'. Christians believe that they must be reborn in a spiritual way, to be forgiven for their sins, in order to enter the Kingdom of God. Together, read the quotations from the Anglican baptism service, discuss what they mean and make notes.

'Child or adult baptism'. Explain the purposes of baptism and focus on the promises made by the godparents. In the baptism of adults, who makes the promises? Discuss why some Christians prefer to have a dedication service for babies and to wait until they are older for baptism.

'Confirmation' can be introduced through discussion of any commitments the students have made, for example, promises or pledges made on joining a group or organisation. Explain that the rights attained with adulthood entail responsibilities. What do people do in order to be committed and responsible? Ask the students to fill in the table, giving ideas of what people should try to do and try not to do in order to keep their promise to serve Christ.

'Funeral' must be introduced sensitively, especially if any students have experienced bereavement. Ask the students what a funeral is for. Write the responses on the flip chart and read aloud parts of a Christian funeral service on the activity sheet. (The biblical quotations on the activity sheet are used in the Anglican funeral service Alternative Service Book.) Ask the students to match the Christian beliefs about death with the words from the funeral service. Ask them to consider what happens when we die and to write about their beliefs and compare them with Christian beliefs.

Plenary

Ask the students what they have learned about the purposes of religious ceremonies for rites of passage, and why these are important to Christians.

Activity sheet – Rites of passage

Baptism symbols

☞ Write the meanings of the baptism symbols. Use the word bank to help. One has been done for you.

Word bank				
cleansing	Crucifixion	dove	Holy Spirit	light
rebirth	sin	washing	water	

Chi-roh
An old Christian symbol from the Greek word for Christ.

Baptism ceremony

 Read these words from the Anglican baptism service.

Discuss them with your group.

On a separate piece of paper, make notes about what they mean.

We who are born of earthly parents need to be born again. In the gospel Jesus tells us that, unless a man has been born again, he cannot see the kingdom of God. God gives us the way to a second birth.	Surround these children with your love; protect them from evil; fill them with your Holy Spirit and receive them into the family of your church.
Repent and be baptised in the name of Jesus Christ for the forgiveness of sins.	You shall receive the gift of the Holy Spirit.
I sign you with the cross, the sign of Christ. *(The priest dips a finger in the water in the font and makes the sign of the cross on the child's forehead.)*	May God Almighty deliver you from the powers of darkness and lead you in the light and obedience of Christ.
We thank you for the gift of water to cleanse us and revive us. Bless this water, that your servants who are washed in it may be made one with Christ.	Receive this light. This is to show that you have passed from darkness to light. *(The priest gives the child, or a godparent, a lighted candle.)*

Child or adult baptism

☞ Read the promises made by godparents at a Christian baptism.

> Do you believe and trust in God the Father, who made the world?
>
> Do you believe and trust in his Son, Jesus Christ, who redeemed mankind?
>
> Do you believe and trust in his Holy Spirit, who gives life to the people of God?

> I believe and trust in him.

☞ Some Christians do not take their children to be baptised when they are very young.

Instead they are baptised when they are grown up.

Which do you think is better?

Discuss this with your group.

Take a vote. Each put a tick in one of the boxes. Count the ticks.

Infant baptism is better	Adult baptism is better

We think _____ baptism is better because _____

_____

_____

_____

Confirmation

Many Christians have a special Confirmation service when they are about 13 years old. They take responsibility for keeping the promises made at their baptism.

Do you believe and trust in God the Father, who made the world?
Do you believe and trust in his Son, Jesus Christ, who redeemed mankind?
Do you believe and trust in his Holy Spirit, who gives life to the people of God?
I believe and trust in him.

Do you turn to Christ?
Do you repent of your sins?
Do you renounce evil?

I turn to Christ.
I repent of my sins.
I renounce evil.

I believe and trust in him.

☞ They promise to serve Christ. List some things they could do to serve him and what they should try not to do.

Try to	Try not to

Funeral

☞ Cut out and match the Christian beliefs about death to the words from the funeral service.

Christian beliefs

Jesus died but came back to life in a different form. When Christians die they will be with Jesus.

When people die they are reborn. Their earthly bodies have died but their spirits live on.

Bodies die but people who believe in Jesus will live forever in some way.

God will look after people in need.

Nothing in the world belongs to us. It belongs to God.

Funeral service

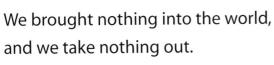

We brought nothing into the world, and we take nothing out.
1 Timothy 6:7

God so loved the world that he gave his only Son, that whoever believes in him should not perish, but have eternal life.
John 3:16

Blessed are those who mourn, for they shall be comforted.
Matthew 5:4

We believe that Jesus died and rose again; and so it will be for those who died as Christians; God will bring them to life with Jesus.
1 Thessalonians 4:14

Someone will ask, 'How are the dead raised? With what kind of body do they come?' You foolish man! What you sow does not come to life unless it dies. And what you sow is not the body which is to be, but a bare kernel, perhaps of wheat or of some other grain. But God gives it a body as he has chosen, and to each kind of seed its own body. So it is with the resurrection of the dead. What is sown can die; what is raised cannot. It is sown a physical body; it is raised a spiritual body.
1 Corinthians 15:35–44

Teacher's notes

Specials!

The universe

Objectives

- Describe Christian beliefs and teachings about creation
- Make comparisons between religion and science
- Select relevant information from written sources to produce coherent answers to questions on the purpose of human life and reflect on their own understanding about it

Prior knowledge

The students should know how people's religion affects their views of the world and take into account scientific understanding when discussing religious teaching. They should also be given opportunities to explore concepts of meaning and to develop skills of empathy, interpretation and reflection and to agree and disagree with others in a constructive way.

QCA link

Unit 9B Where did the universe come from?

Scottish attainment targets

Christianity
Strand – Sacred writings, stories and key figures
Level D;
Personal search
Strand – The natural world
Level D

Background

The Creation story is the biblical myth of the origin of the universe in which God creates order from the chaos of infinite, formless waters. Some Christians believe that it is literally true; others find it incredible but believe that the universe came into being according to God's design.

Starter activity

Ask the students to discuss the question 'Which came first – the chicken or the egg?' Where did the first egg come from? Where did the first chicken come from? Read or sing the hymn *All Things Bright and Beautiful*. What answers are suggested by this hymn?

Activity sheets

'What came first?' requires the students to cut out and rank the pictures in order of what came first. If they are not sure which came first, they should rank items equally. Encourage them to make decisions based on logic.

'Genesis' should be tackled in the same way as 'What came first?' The students should cut out the pictures and text and arrange them in chronological order. They can check their answers in Genesis 1:1–26.

'The image of God.' Ask the students to read the passage and to answer the questions. Explain the Christian view that resembling God does not mean a physical but a spiritual likeness and that responsibilities come with dominion over other animals. The students could give examples of how people should fulfil these responsibilities. Some of them might interpret 'I have provided all kinds of grain and all kinds of fruit for you to eat' as an instruction to eat only plants and not to kill animals. The students could discuss and write about the ways in which modern humans are fulfilling or failing to fulfil their responsibilities for the world.

'The scientist and the theist'. Ensure that the students understand that theists believe in one God who created the universe. Encourage them to think of both sides of the argument concerning the creation of the universe by filling in the speech bubbles.

Plenary

Ask the students to consider their own views about how the universe was created and the role, if any, played by God. Can they find any universal truths in the creation story in Genesis?

Activity sheet – The universe

What came first?

☞ Which things were here first? Cut out the pictures and put them in chronological order.

very long ago ⟶ present day

moon   wheel   planets

mobile phone   Earth   woman

baby   trees   sea

land   man   fish

birds   mammals   Sun

Activity sheet – The universe

Genesis

These verses are from the book of Genesis in the Bible.

☞ Which came first?

Cut them out and put them in order.

Compare this with your answers for 'What came first?'

God commanded, 'Let the water be filled with living beings and let the air be filled with birds' – and it was done. He blessed them and told them to reproduce.

God commanded, 'Let the earth produce all kinds of animal life; domestic and wild, large and small' – and it was done. God said, 'Now we will make human beings.'

God commanded, 'Let there be a dome to divide the water and keep it in two separate places. So God made a dome. It separated the water under it from the water above it. He named it 'sky'.

The Earth was formless. The raging ocean that covered everything was in darkness. God commanded, 'Let there be light' – and there was light. God separated the light from darkness, and he named the light 'day' and the darkness 'night'.

God commanded, 'Let the water below the sky come together in one place, so that land will appear' – and it was done. He named the land 'Earth' and the water 'sea'. God commanded, 'Let the Earth produce plants, those that bear grain and those that bear fruit' – and it was done.

God commanded, 'Let lights appear in the sky to separate day from night and to show when days, years and festivals begin; they will shine in the sky to give light to the Earth' – and it was done. So God made two larger lights, the Sun to rule over the day and the moon to rule over the night; he also made the stars.

Specials! RE Christianity

The image of God

☞ Read the passage from the book of Genesis.

Then God said, 'Now we will make human beings; they will be like us and resemble us. They will have power over the fish, the birds, and all animals, domestic and wild, large and small.'

So God created human beings, making them to be like himself. He created them male and female, blessed them and said, 'Have many children, so that your descendants will live all over the Earth and bring it under their control. I am putting you in charge of the fish, the birds and all the wild animals. I have provided all kinds of grain and all kinds of fruit for you to eat; but for all the wild animals and for all the birds I have provided grass and leafy plants for food' – and it was done.

Genesis 1:26–30

☞ Discuss these questions with your group.
Write the answers in the boxes.

1. In what ways are humans like God?

2. What power did God give to humans?

3. What responsibilities should come with this power?

The scientist and the theist

☞ What might the scientist say about the creation of the universe and everything in it?

What might the theist say about all this?

Write their arguments in the speech bubbles.

A theist believes in a God who created the universe and all living things.

Theist

Scientist

Specials! RE Christianity

© Folens (copiable page)

Teacher's notes

Suffering

Objectives

- Give examples of different kinds of suffering
- Know a Bible story about suffering and explain in simple terms how and why Jesus suffered
- Give a simple explanation of the Christian view of suffering and state their own views
- Know something about an individual, charity or belief which seeks to combat suffering or care for people who are suffering

Prior knowledge

The students should know the technical terminology used in Christianity and weigh up and evaluate different responses to an issue. They should also understand the basic Christian beliefs about God, people and the world.

QCA link

Unit 9C Why do we suffer?

Scottish attainment targets

Personal search
Strand – Relationships and moral values
Level D;
Christianity
Strand – Beliefs
Level E

Background

The message of the Bible is that people are responsible beings and that if they choose evil instead of good, they and others suffer the consequences. The Bible emphasises strongly the link between suffering and evil. Some Christians believe that all suffering is caused by sin – even natural disasters (because God punishes humanity rather than individuals). This belief arises from the belief that humanity is corrupt. This belief is founded on 'the Fall' – the sin of Adam and Eve (Genesis 3), which corrupted God's perfect creation. Most Christians believe that God does not control the events of the universe – that people have free will.

Starter activity

On the flip chart, write the word 'suffering' and ask the students to give some examples of suffering. What might the sufferers feel, apart from sadness, pain and grief? They might feel angry and want revenge or they might feel compassion for other sufferers and want to help them. Discuss some of the actions people take after they have suffered.

Activity sheets

'In the news' asks the students to identify the causes of the suffering of people affected by the events in the news reports. Ask them whether this suffering could have been prevented. How?

'In the Bible (1)' and 'In the Bible (2)'. The students should read the Bible story of Job and the stories about the Garden of Eden and Noah. Ask them to complete the chart after reading each story. They should say who sufferered, why they suffered and what this says about God. Was it fair? For example, students might think God was testing Job or that he was sure of Job's faith and wanted to show that goodness can defeat evil. What can be learnt from the stories about the Christian view of suffering? Explain that devout Christians do not blame God for suffering but that they sometimes regard it as a test of their faith in God or consider that it is a punishment for sin.

'Help from Christians' encourages the students to find out about Christian groups such as CAFOD, Christian Aid, Prospects, Tearfund, and CARE. Which groups of people do they help? (For example, elderly people, young people, people in developing countries.) What kinds of suffering do they try to alleviate? (For example, poverty, disease, natural disasters, lack of basic human rights.) How do they help? (For example, collecting money, spending time with people, putting pressure on governments.) The students should then conclude what difference the group makes to the lives of sufferers.

Plenary

Ask the students if they think anyone deserves to suffer. Is it fair that people suffer when they do not deserve to? Ask them to explain how Christian belief helps people to endure suffering, and discuss how suffering could produce something good. Remind them of the ultimate Christian suffering – that of Christ on the Cross – and its purpose.

In the news

 Read the news reports with your group. Who is suffering? Think about the people mentioned here and others, not mentioned, who might also be suffering.
Was this caused by people or by natural causes?
Write your answers on a separate piece of paper.

No joy in ride

Four teenagers died yesterday when their stolen car travelling at 100mph crashed into a lamp post. The two girls and two boys, aged between 13 and 16, had been drinking cider, lager and vodka in a cemetery before stealing the Ford Ka from the Rex Cinema car park.

Afghans kill British soldier

A British soldier was killed and five others wounded in a gun battle with Afghan rebels near Mazar-e-Sharif in northern Afghanistan yesterday.

Village mourns six year old

St John's church was full and the churchyard was packed with villagers paying their last respects to little Lynne Smith, who died, aged 6, last week after a long battle against cancer. Lynne spent much of her short life in hospital.

Quake victims

The death toll from the earthquake in Pakistan on Saturday has risen to 30 000. Entire villages in the hills have been flattened by the earthquake, leaving hundreds of thousands of people without shelter, food or medicines. Many survivors are sleeping in the open in sub-zero temperatures.

Children deprived

A new UNICEF report, The State of the World's Children 2005, shows that more than half of the world's children are suffering from poverty, war or HIV/AIDS.

Specials! RE Christianity

In the Bible (1)

☞ Read the stories from the Bible on this page and 'In the Bible (2)'.

Discuss them with your group.

There was a man named Job, who worshipped God. He was a good man. He had seven sons and three daughters and owned 7000 sheep, 3000 camels, 1000 cattle and 500 donkeys. He had many servants and was the richest man in the East.

One day God said to Satan, 'There is no one on Earth as faithful as my servant Job. He worships me and does nothing evil.'

'It is easy for him to worship you. You look after him and his family and everything he owns. He would not worship you if you took away everything he has,' said Satan.

One day, raiders killed all Job's workers in the fields, apart from one who came to tell him that all the camels had been stolen and their riders killed. As he was speaking, another arrived and said that all Job's children had been killed by a storm which destroyed the house where they were at a feast.

Job tore his clothes in grief. He threw himself onto the ground saying, 'I was born with nothing and I shall die with nothing. The Lord gives and now he has taken away. May his name be praised!'

Later God said to Satan, 'There is no one on Earth as good and faithful as Job. You persuaded me to harm him for no reason, but he is still faithful.'

Satan answered, 'A person will give up everything in order to stay alive. If you harm his body he will curse you!'

One day Job woke up with sores all over his body. His wife said, 'Why are you faithful to God, when he has let this happen?'

Job said, 'When God sends good things we welcome them. We cannot complain about the bad ones.'

Whatever anyone said, Job would not curse God. He praised him and stayed faithful. Many years later God healed Job's sores. Job began to farm again. God blessed Job in his old age. He had 14 000 sheep, 6000 camels, 2000 cattle and 1000 donkeys. He had seven sons and three daughters and lived to a great age.

Job 1–2; 42:12, 16

Activity sheet – Suffering

In the Bible (2)

God created a beautiful garden. He put a man and a woman in the garden. They were naked but this was natural for them. God told them that they could eat the fruit of any tree in the garden – except one. This was the tree which gives knowledge of what is good and what is bad. But they disobeyed God: they ate the forbidden fruit. They wanted to be wise. When God found out, he sent them out of the garden. He told the woman that from then on women would have great pain in childbirth. He told the man that he would no longer enjoy the garden but would have to work hard on the land. He said, 'You were made from soil and you will become soil again.' Then God put creatures with flaming swords to guard the garden.

Genesis 3

When the Lord saw how wicked everyone on Earth was, he was sorry that he had ever made them. He said, 'I will wipe out these people I have created.' But he spoke to Noah: 'You are the only one in the world who does what is right. I am going to send a flood to destroy all the others. You must build a boat and take your family on to it. Take two of every kind of animal – a male and a female.' The flood came and destroyed everyone. When the water went down, Noah and his family were the only people left on Earth. A rainbow appeared in the sky. God said that this was a symbol of his promise never again to destroy the human race.

Genesis 6–9:13

☞ Make notes in the chart about what the Bible teaches about suffering and about God.

Story	Who suffered?	Why?	What this says about God
Job			
The Garden of Eden			
Noah			

Specials! RE Christianity © Folens (copiable page)

Help from Christians

☞ Find out about a Christian group which helps people who are suffering.
Write notes on the table below.

Name of group:		
Sufferers (age group, where they live)	**Types of suffering**	**How the group helps them**

☞ What difference does this group make to the lives of sufferers?

_____

_____

_____

_____

_____

Assessment sheet

Specials!

Topic _____

At the start

I knew _____

_____

I could _____

_____

Now

I have learned _____

_____

_____

_____

I can _____

_____

Next

I need to find out _____

_____

_____

I need to work on _____

_____

Specials! RE Christianity © Folens (copiable page)